All the tunes you've ever wanted to play...

BOOK TWO

All the tunes you've ever wanted to play... BOOK TWO

One hundred favourite melodies
for B flat instruments including Clarinet
Trumpet, Cornet and Tenor Sax

Kevin Mayhew

We hope you enjoy *All the tunes you've ever wanted to play* (Book 2)
for B♭ instruments. Further copies of this and the other books
in the series are available from your local music shop.

In case of difficulty, please contact the publisher direct:

The Sales Department
KEVIN MAYHEW LTD
Rattlesden
Bury St Edmunds
Suffolk IP30 0SZ

Phone 01449 737978
Fax 01449 737834

Please ask for our complete catalogue of outstanding Instrumental Music.

Acknowledgements

The publishers wish to express their gratitude to the copyright owners for
permission to use copyright material in this book. Details of these are given
underneath the individual tunes. All other tunes are copyright Kevin Mayhew Ltd.

Every effort has been made to trace the owners of copyright material, and we hope
that no copyright has been infringed. Pardon is sought and apology made if the
contrary be the case, and a correction will be made in any reprint of this book.

First published in Great Britain in 1995 by Kevin Mayhew Ltd

© Copyright 1995 Kevin Mayhew Ltd

ISBN 0 86209 614 6
Catalogue No: 3611147

Cover design by Roy Mitchell
Music edited and arranged by Donald Thomson
Music Setting: Daniel Kelly

Printed and bound in Great Britain

Contents

Arranger's Note

The tunes in this book have been arranged for
B♭ instruments. Although the melody line may be
played alone, accompanying chords for use by
keyboard or guitar players have also been provided.
Where necessary, an easier version for guitar using a
capo is shown below the keyboard chords.

EARLY ONE MORNING
Traditional English Melody

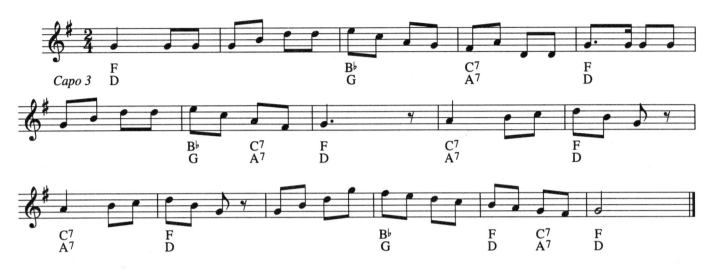

VALSE LENTE from 'COPPÉLIA'
Léo Delibes

IT'S A LONG WAY TO TIPPERARY
Jack Judge and Harry Williams

FÜR ELISE

Ludwig van Beethoven

MY LOVE IS LIKE A RED, RED ROSE

Traditional Scottish Melody

♩ = daat = 1 beat
♩♫ = daddy = ½ + ½

SAILORS' HORNPIPE
Sea Shanty

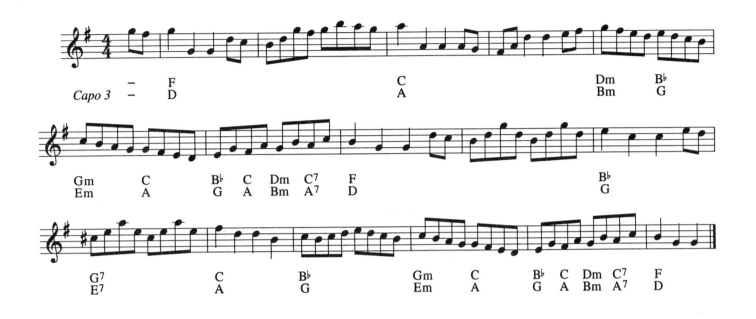

Capo 3

—	F				C		Dm	B♭
—	D				A		Bm	G

Gm	C	B♭	C	Dm	C⁷	F		B♭
Em	A	G	A	Bm	A⁷	D		G

G⁷	C	B♭	Gm	C	B♭	C	Dm	C⁷	F
E⁷	A	G	Em	A	G	A	Bm	A⁷	D

LET'S ALL GO DOWN THE STRAND
Harry Castling and C W Murphy

Capo 1

E♭		Cm	
D		Bm	

B♭⁷	E♭	D	Gm	B♭⁷
A⁷	D	C♯	F♯m	A⁷

E♭	Cm	A♭	G
D	Bm	G	F♯

Cm	Gm	Cm	Gm	B♭⁷	E♭	B♭⁷	E♭
Bm	F♯m	Bm	F♯m	A⁷	D	A⁷	D

9

SKATERS' WALTZ
Emile Waldteufel

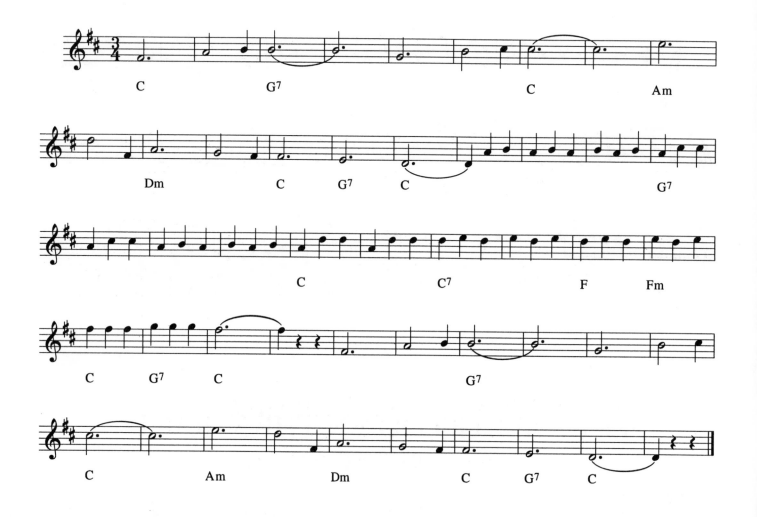

GIRLS AND BOYS
Traditional Melody

THE CAN CAN
Jacques Offenbach

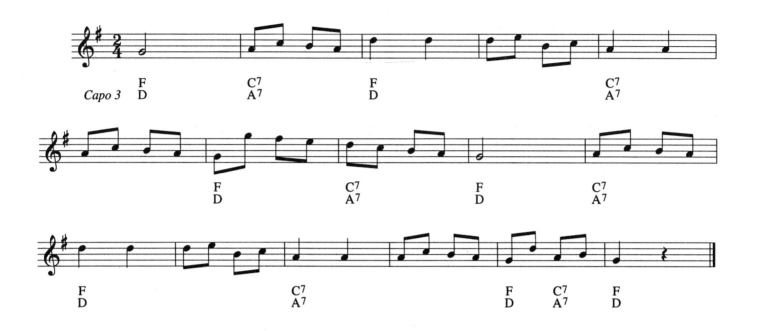

YE BANKS AND BRAES
Traditional Scottish Melody

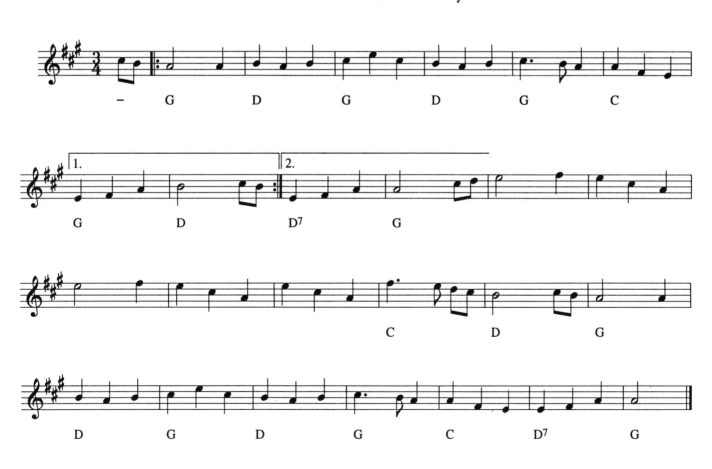

KP
14/6/00

IF YOU'RE HAPPY AND YOU KNOW IT
Traditional Melody

CLAIR DE LUNE
Claude Debussy

HERE WE GO ROUND THE MULBERRY BUSH
Traditional Melody

THE MARSEILLAISE
French National Anthem

O FOR THE WINGS OF A DOVE
Felix Mendelssohn

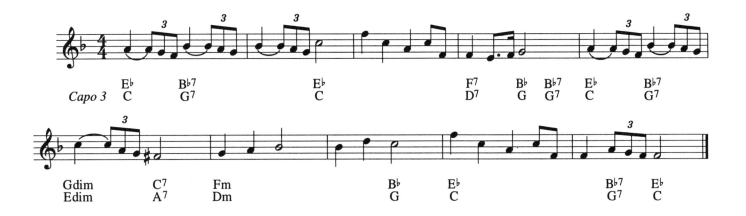

WALTZ from 'THE MERRY WIDOW'

Franz Lehar

COME, LANDLORD, FILL THE FLOWING BOWL

Traditional Melody

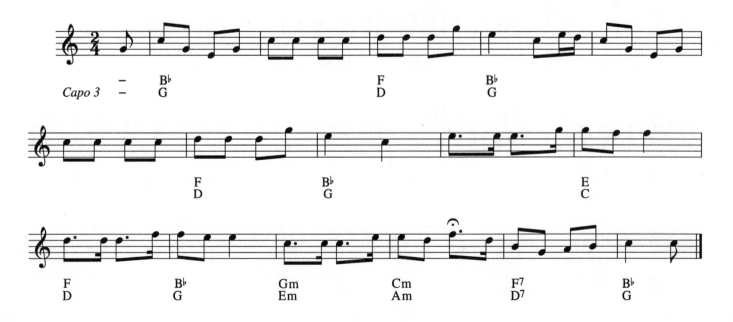

ROW YOUR BOAT
Traditional Melody

NESSUN DORMA
Giocomo Puccini

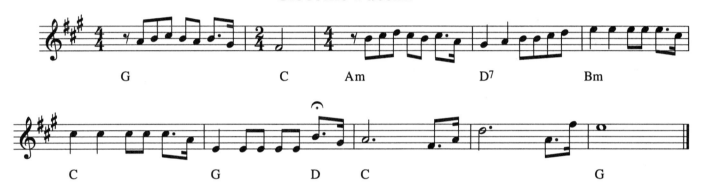

THE VICAR OF BRAY
Traditional Melody

AFTER THE BALL
Charles Harris

NOBODY KNOWS THE TROUBLE I SEE
Spiritual

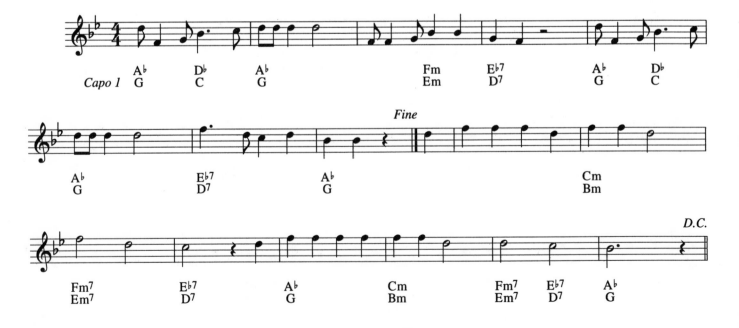

I'VE GOT A LOVELY BUNCH OF COCONUTS
Fred Heatherton

PRELUDE
Frédéric Chopin

PIZZICATO POLKA
Johann Strauss

SWEET AND LOW
Joseph Barnby

PANIS ANGELICUS
César Franck

THERE IS A TAVERN IN THE TOWN
Traditional Melody

THE STAR SPANGLED BANNER

John Stafford Smith

ON WINGS OF SONG

Felix Mendelssohn

RADETZKY MARCH
Johann Strauss

THE OLD FOLKS AT HOME
Stephen Foster

THE LINCOLNSHIRE POACHER
Traditional Melody

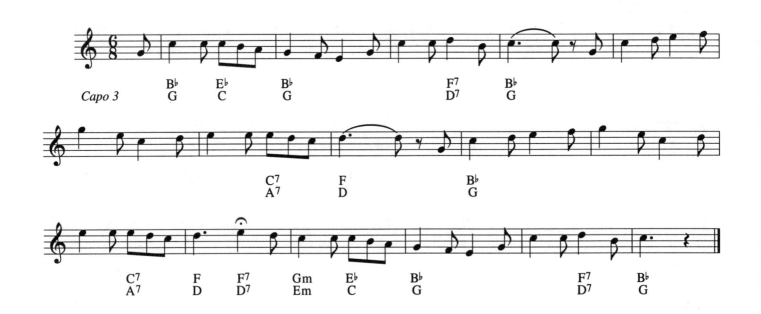

AVE MARIA
Franz Schubert

BELIEVE ME IF ALL THOSE ENDEARING YOUNG CHARMS

Thomas Moore

LULLABY

Johannes Brahms

STEAL AWAY
Spiritual

MELODY
Anton Rubinstein

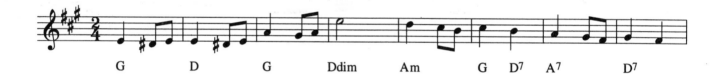

SCARBOROUGH FAIR
Traditional English Melody

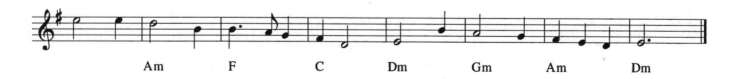

IN THE SHADE OF THE OLD APPLE TREE

Harry Williams

AIR from SUITE NO 3

Johann Sebastian Bach

25

MAPLE LEAF RAG
Scott Joplin

TRUMPET TUNE
Henry Purcell

26

PLAISIR D'AMOUR

Giovanni Paolo Martini

THE YELLOW ROSE OF TEXAS

Traditional Melody

THE LASS OF RICHMOND HILL

James Hook

WHEN I SURVEY THE WONDROUS CROSS

Edward Miller

GALWAY BAY
Arthur Colahan

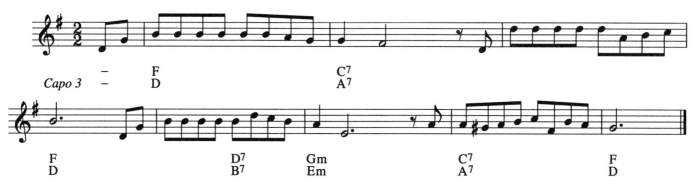

MARCHE MILITAIRE
Franz Schubert

JOHN PEEL
Traditional Melody

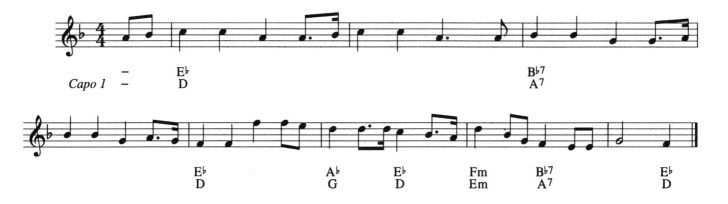

BARCAROLLE
Jacques Offenbach

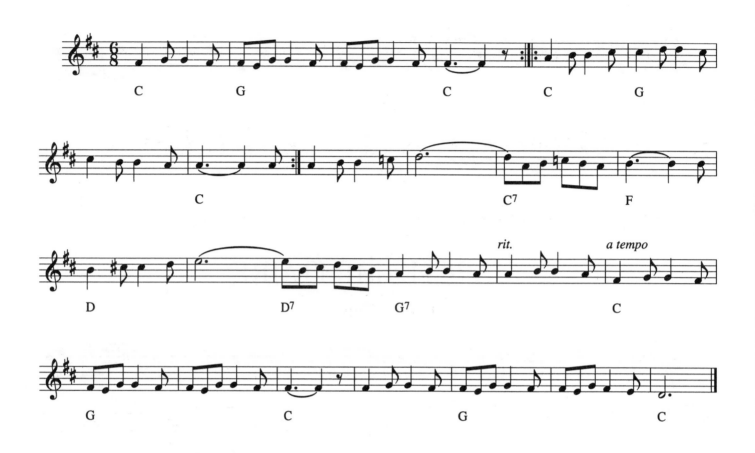

OH SUSANNA
Stephen Foster

THE KEEL ROW
Traditional Melody

O SOLE MIO
Eduardo di Capua

LILLIBURLERO
Traditional Melody

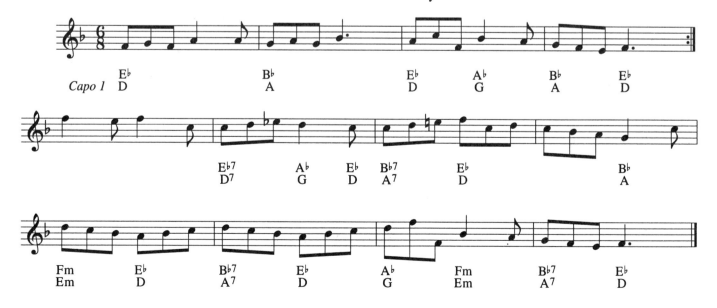

WALTZ from 'DIE FLEDERMAUS'
Johann Strauss

SHE'LL BE COMIN' ROUND THE MOUNTAIN
Traditional Melody

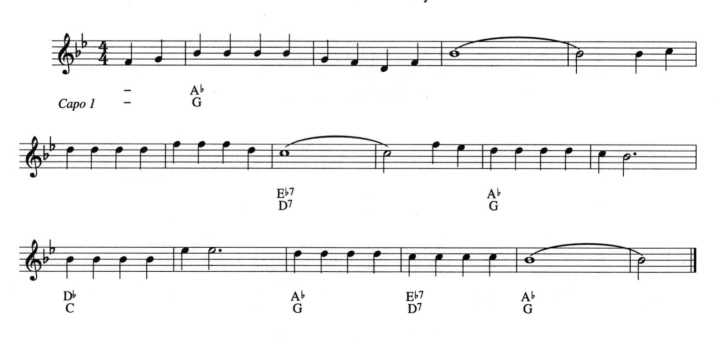

HE'S GOT THE WHOLE WORLD IN HIS HAND
Traditional Melody

DEEP RIVER
Spiritual

CHERRY RIPE
Charles Edward Horn

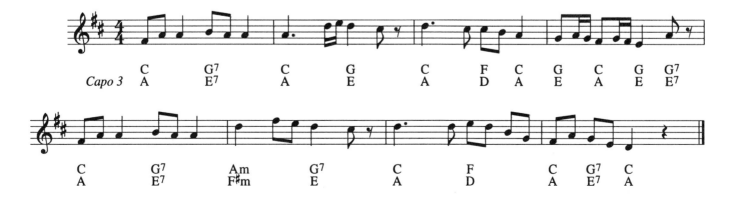

MY BONNIE LIES OVER THE OCEAN
Traditional Melody

ALL PEOPLE THAT ON EARTH DO DWELL
From the *Genevan Psalter*

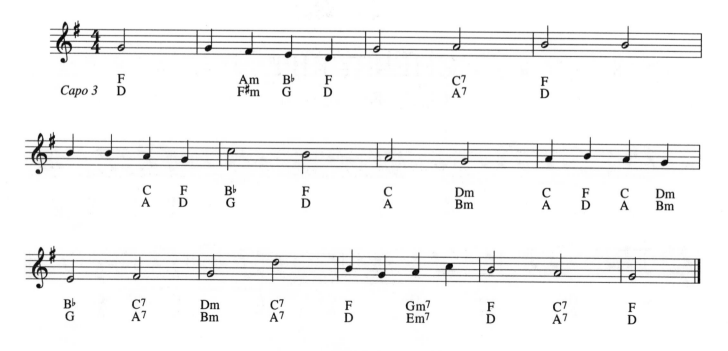

TRITSCH TRATSCH POLKA

Johann Strauss

THE SOLDIERS' CHORUS from 'FAUST'

Charles Gounod

BLOW THE WIND SOUTHERLY

Traditional Melody

AVE MARIA
Charles Gounod

OH WHERE HAS MY LITTLE DOG GONE?
Traditional Melody

THREE BLIND MICE
Traditional Melody

ROMANZA
Anon

THE MAN WHO BROKE THE BANK
AT MONTE CARLO
Fred Gilbert

DASHING AWAY WITH THE
SMOOTHING IRON

Traditional Melody

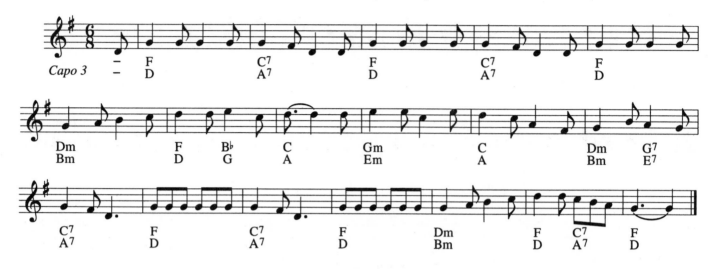

DADDY WOULDN'T BUY ME A BOW-WOW

Joseph Tabrar

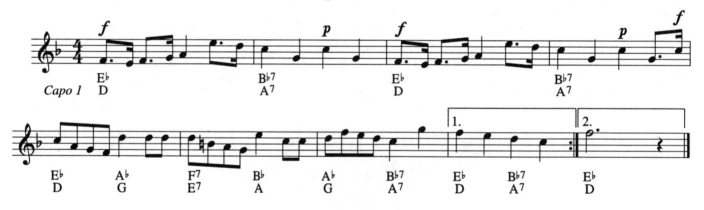

LIEBESTRAUM

Franz Liszt

DOWN BY THE RIVERSIDE
Spiritual

WALTZ
Johannes Brahms

JEANIE WITH THE LIGHT BROWN HAIR

Stephen Foster

THE BLUE BELL OF SCOTLAND

Traditional Scottish Melody

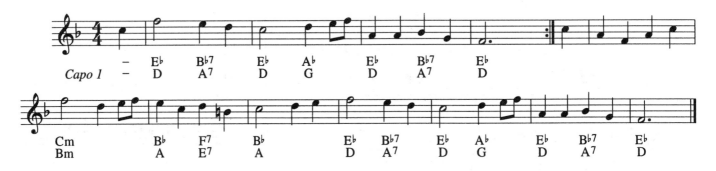

TIT-WILLOW from 'THE MIKADO'

Arthur Sullivan

POLOVTSIAN DANCE
Alexander Borodin

ON ILKLEY MOOR BAHT 'AT
Traditional Melody

WI' A HUNDRED PIPERS
Traditional Scottish Melody

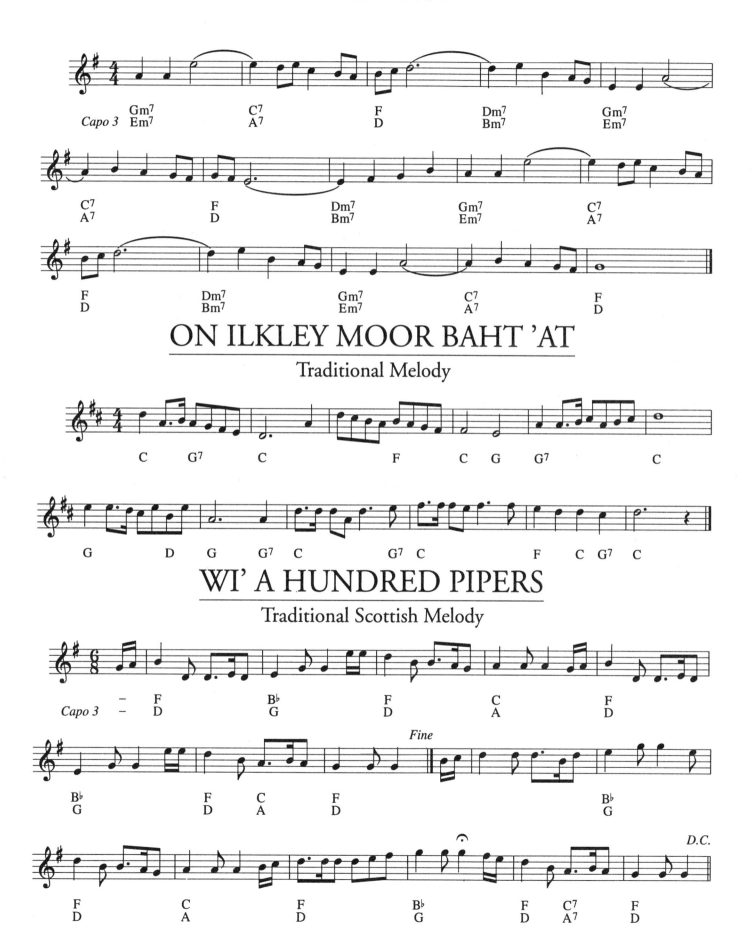

COCKLES AND MUSSELS
Traditional Irish Melody

TRÄUMERAI
Robert Schumann

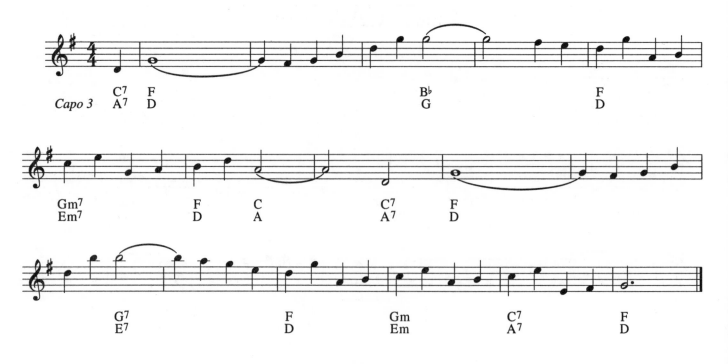

THE GRAND OLD DUKE OF YORK

Traditional Melody

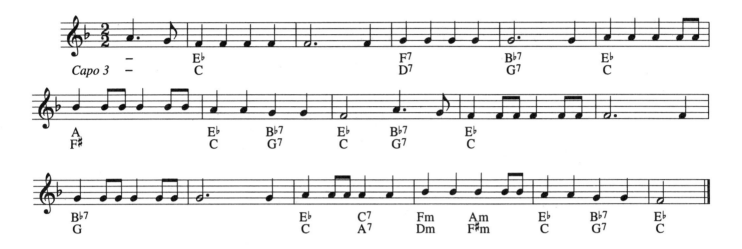

CHARLIE IS MY DARLING

Traditional Scottish Melody

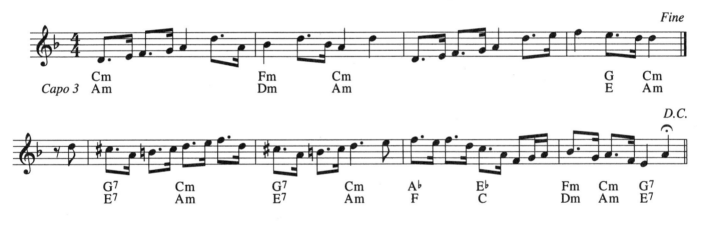

OH DEAR, WHAT CAN THE MATTER BE ?

Traditional Melody

CAMPTOWN RACES
Stephen Foster

THEME from PATHÉTIQUE SONATA
Ludwig van Beethoven

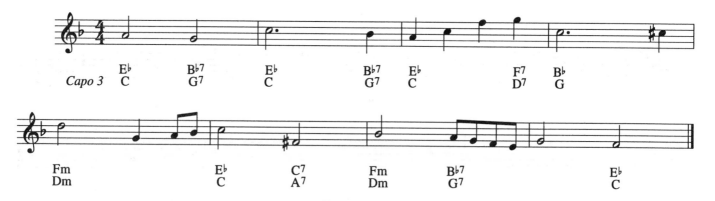

COMING THROUGH THE RYE
Traditional Scottish Melody

DANCE OF THE SUGAR-PLUM FAIRY

Peter Ilyich Tchaikovsky

THIS OLD MAN

Anon

THE CAMPBELLS ARE COMING

Traditional Scottish Melody

DANCE OF THE HOURS
Amilcare Ponchielli

BARBARA ALLEN
Traditional English Melody

CAPRICE
Nicolo Paganini

AVE VERUM CORPUS
Wolfgang Amadeus Mozart

DRINK TO ME ONLY WITH THINE EYES
Colonel R Mellish

ON TOP OF OLD SMOKEY
Traditional Melody

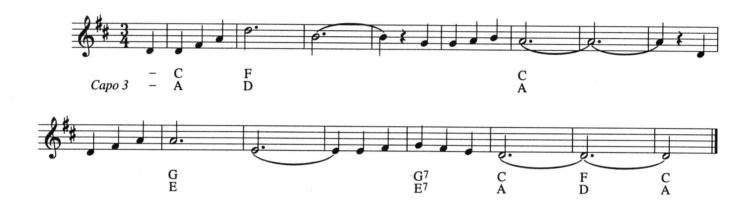

THE LAST ROSE OF SUMMER
Traditional Irish Melody